This book belongs to ...

....

OXFORD
UNIVERSITY PRESS

Great Clarendon Street, Oxford, OX2 6DP,
United Kingdom

Oxford University Press is a department of the University of Oxford.
It furthers the University's objective of excellence in research, scholarship,
and education by publishing worldwide. Oxford is a registered trade mark of
Oxford University Press in the UK and in certain other countries

ISBN: 978-0-19-273431-0

3 5 7 9 10 8 6 4

Typeset in Edbaskerville

Paper used in the production of this book is a natural, recyclable product made
from wood grown in sustainable forests. The manufacturing process conforms
to the environmental regulations of the country of origin.

Acknowledgements;
Series Editors: Kate Ruttle, Annemarie Young

READ WITH
**Biff,
Chip &
Kipper**

Floppy and the Bone

and Other Stories

OXFORD
UNIVERSITY PRESS

Tips for Reading Together

Children learn best when reading is fun.

- Talk about the title and the picture on page 7.
- Identify the letter patterns *ch* and *ss* in the title and talk about the sounds they make when you read them.
- Look at the *ch* and *oo* words on page 8. Say the sounds in each word and then say the word (e.g. *s-u-ch, such*; *s-oo-n, soon*).
- Read the story then find the words with *ch*, *oo* and *v*.
- Talk about the story and do the fun activities at the end of the book.

Children enjoy re-reading stories and this helps to build their confidence.

Have fun!

After you have read the story, find the five worms hidden in the pictures.

The main sounds practised in this book are 'ch' as in *Chip*, 'oo' as in *too*, and 'v' as in *Viv*.

For more hints and tips on helping your child become a successful and enthusiastic reader look at our website www.oxfordowl.co.uk.

Such a Fuss

Written by Roderick Hunt
Illustrated by Nick Schon,
based on the original characters
created by Roderick Hunt and Alex Brychta

OXFORD
UNIVERSITY PRESS

Read these words

Chip   too

whi**ch**   s**oo**n

mu**ch**   c**oo**l

Dad had six hens.

Chip had a hen, too.

"This is Viv," said Chip.

Biff got the eggs.

She put them in a box.

The hens ran up.

Chip fed them.

"Viv is upset," said Chip.

"Such a fuss," said Biff.

17

Chip put the hens to bed.

But Viv did not go in.

Biff and Chip hid in the shed.

A fox got in.

The fox ran off.

"I can soon fix the pen,"
said Dad.

"Viv is a cool hen," said Chip.

Talk about the story

Who has six hens?

What is Chip's hen called?

Why was Viv upset?

What kind of pet would you like to have?

Missing letters

Choose an ending for the words.

ri <u>ch</u>　　　　fo <u>x</u>　　　　mu<u>ch</u>

si <u>x</u>　　　　su <u>ch</u>　　　　bo <u>x</u>

Tips for Reading Together

Children learn best when reading is fun.

- Talk about the title and the picture on page 29.
- Identify the letter pattern *sh* in the title and talk about the sound it makes when you read it.
- Look at the *sh* words on page 30. Say the sounds in each word and then say the word (e.g. *sh-e-d, shed*).
- Read the story then find the words beginning with *sh*.
- Talk about the story and do the fun activities at the end of the book.

Children enjoy re-reading stories and this helps to build their confidence.

Have fun!

After you have read the story, find five grasshoppers hidden in the pictures.

The main sound practised in this book is 'sh' as in *shop*. Other sounds practised are 'i', 'o' and 'a' as in *ship*, *shop* and *hat*.

For more hints and tips on helping your child become a successful and enthusiastic reader look at our website www.oxfordowl.co.uk.

Shops

Written by Roderick Hunt
Illustrated by Alex Brychta

OXFORD
UNIVERSITY PRESS

Read these words

shop   ship

shell   shed

shut   shall

Sam had a shop.

"I sell shells," she said.

Pam had a shop.

"This is a ship shop,"
she said.

Pat had a hat shop.

"I sell hats," she said.

"Then I will get a hat,"
said Kipper.

"Shall I get that big hat ...

... this cap ...

38

… that red hat …

… this top hat?"

"This shop is shut,"
said Tom.

"This is a pan shop,"
said Tim.

"I sell pans," he said.

et that pan,"
r.

"This shed is a shop,"
said Chip.

44

"I will g
said Kippe nop," said Biff.

"Buns," said Kipper.

Talk about the story

What did Sam sell in her shop?

Who had the ship shop?

Which shop would you like to visit?

What would you like to sell in a shop?

What's in the picture?

What can you find in the picture that begins
with *sh, p, d, b, g, h?*

Tips for Reading Together

Children learn best when reading is fun.

- Talk about the title and the picture on page 51.

- Look through the pictures together and discuss what you think the story might be about.

- Read the story together, pointing to each word and inviting your child to join in.

- Give lots of praise as your child reads with you, and help them when necessary.

- Enjoy re-reading the story and encourage your child to say the repeated phrases with you.

Children enjoy re-reading stories and this helps to build their confidence.

Have fun!

After you have read the story, find the butterfly hidden in every picture.

This book includes these useful common words:
said   the   went   saw

For more hints and tips on helping your child become a successful and enthusiastic reader look at our website www.oxfordowl.co.uk.

Floppy and the Bone

Written by Cynthia Rider,
based on the original characters
created by Roderick Hunt and Alex Brychta
Illustrated by Alex Brychta

OXFORD

UNIVERSITY PRESS

Floppy saw a big bone.

"I want that bone,"
said Floppy.

He got the bone!

"Stop! Stop!" said Biff.

"Drop the bone!" said Chip.

But Floppy did not stop,
and he did not drop the bone!

He ran up the hill.

He ran into a wood...

and onto a bridge...
and he stopped!

Floppy looked down.

He saw a dog in the water.

The dog had a big bone.

Floppy wanted that bone, too.

Grrrrrrrr!
went Floppy.

SPLASH! went the bone.
SPLASH! went Floppy.

"Oh no!" said Floppy.

"The dog I saw was me!"

Talk about the story

Why do you think Floppy took the bone?

What did Floppy see in the water? Did he think it was a real dog?

Do you think Floppy was a sensible dog in this story?

Have you ever wanted something as much as Floppy wanted his bone?

Picture puzzle

How many things can you find beginning with the same sound as the 'b' in ball?

(Answer to picture puzzle: ball, bike, bottle, bowl, boy, bush, butterfly)

Tips for Reading Together

Children learn best when reading is fun.

- Talk about the title and the picture on page 73.

- Look through the pictures together and discuss what you think the story might be about.

- Read the story together, pointing to each word and inviting your child to join in.

- Give lots of praise as your child reads with you, and help them when necessary.

- Enjoy re-reading the story and encourage your child to say the repeated phrases with you.

Children enjoy re-reading stories and this helps to build their confidence.

Have fun!

After you have read the story, find the ladybird hidden in every picture.

This book includes these useful common words:
said   took   look

For more hints and tips on helping your child become a successful and enthusiastic reader look at our website www.oxfordowl.co.uk.

Poor Old Rabbit

Written by Cynthia Rider,
based on the original characters
created by Roderick Hunt and Alex Brychta
Illustrated by Alex Brychta

OXFORD
UNIVERSITY PRESS

73

Floppy saw a toy rabbit.

"Poor old rabbit,"
said Floppy.

"Nobody wants it."

Floppy took it to Kipper.

"Poor old rabbit,"
said Kipper.

Kipper took it to Mum.

"Look at this rabbit,"
said Kipper.

"Nobody wants it."

"Look at this rabbit,"
said Mum.

Dad washed it.

Kipper brushed it.

Chip and Wilma mended it.

They all wanted it now.

Oh no!

"Poor old rabbit,"
said Kipper.

Talk about the story

Why do you think somebody has put the rabbit in the bin?

Why isn't it always safe to take toys out of the bin in the park?

Why did everybody want the rabbit at the end of the story?

What is your favourite toy? What would you do if it got old and torn?

A maze

Help Kipper to get to the rabbit.

Read with Biff, Chip and Kipper
The UK's best-selling home reading series

Phonics

First Stories

	Phonics	First Stories
Level 1 Getting ready to read	Kipper's Alphabet I Spy · Chip's Letter Sounds · Biff's Wonder Words · Floppy's Fun Phonics	Get On · Floppy Did This! · Up You Go · Six in a Bed
Level 2 Starting to read	I am Kipper · Cat in a Bag · The Red Hen · The Fizz-Buzz	Funny Fish · Silly Races! · The Snowman · Dad's Birthday
Level 3 Becoming a reader	Such a Fuss · Shops · The Sing Song · The Backpack	Poor Old Rabbit · I Can Trick a Tiger · Super Dad · Floppy and the Bone
Level 4 Developing as a reader	Wet Feet · The Moon Jet · The Red Goat · Quick! Quick!	Missing! · The Raft Race · Dragon Danger · The Spaceship
Level 5 Building confidence in reading	Egg Fried Rice · Craig Saves the Day · Seasick · Dolphin Rescue	Hungry Floppy · Husky Adventure · Trapped! · Looking after Gran
Level 6 Reading with confidence	Gran's New Blue Shoes · Ice City · Save Pudding Wood · Uncle Max	Hairy-Scary Monster · Mountain Rescue · The Lost Voice · Secret of the Sands

Phonics stories help children practise their sounds and letters, as they learn to do in school.

First Stories have been specially written to provide practice in reading everyday language.

Read with Biff, Chip and Kipper Collections:

Up You Go and Other Stories · Six in a Bed and Other Stories · Funny Fish and Other Stories · The Fizz-Buzz and Other Stories

Floppy and the Bone and Other Stories · I Can Trick a Tiger and Other Stories · The Moon Jet and Other Stories · Dragon Danger and Other Stories

2 Phonics and 2 First Stories in every collection

Phonics support

Flashcards are a really fun way to practise phonics and build reading skills. **Age 3+**

My Phonics Kit is designed to support you and your child as you practise phonics together at home. It includes stickers, workbooks, interactive eBooks, support for parents and more! **Age 5+**

Read Write Inc. Phonics: A range of fun rhyming stories to support decoding skills. **Age 4+**

Songbirds Phonics: Lively and engaging phonics stories from Children's Laureate, Julia Donaldson. **Age 4+**

Help your child's reading with essential tips, advice on phonics and free eBooks
www.oxforddowl.co.uk